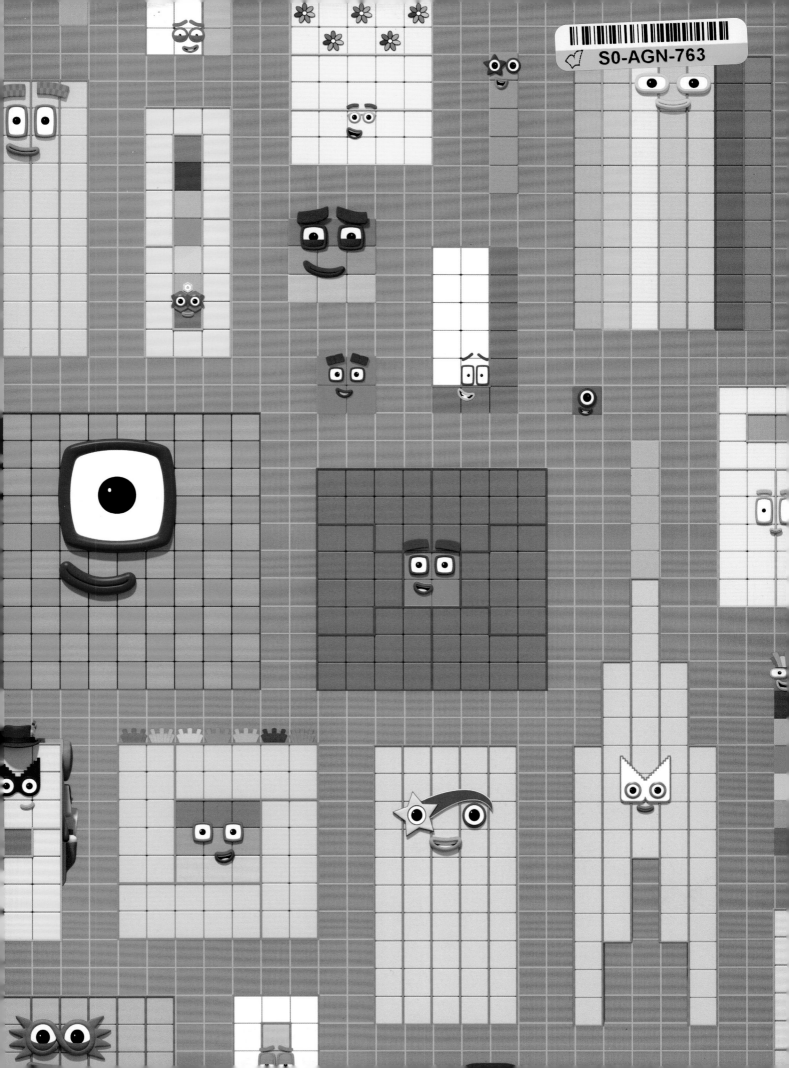

This book
belongs to
- - - - - - - - - - -

Published by Sweet Cherry Publishing Limited
Unit 36, Vulcan House,
Vulcan Road,
Leicester, LE5 3EF
United Kingdom

Published in 2021

2 4 6 8 10 9 7 5 3 1

ISBN: 978-1-78226-601-3

Written by Tori Cotton

www.sweetcherrypublishing.com

Printed and manufactured in Turkey
T.L010

ANNUAL 2022

100

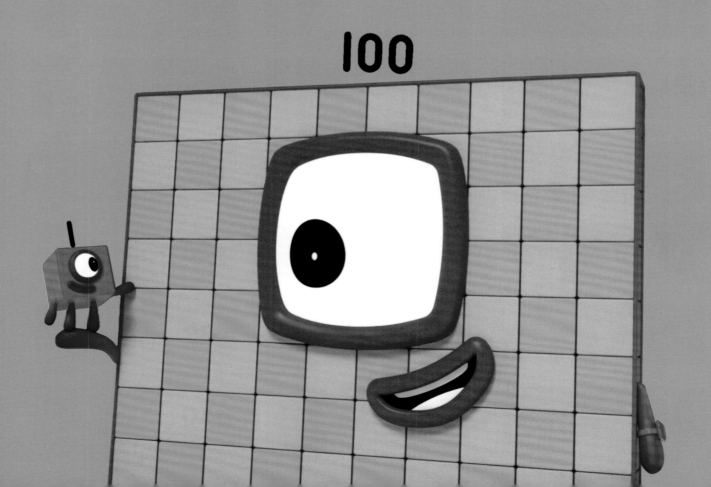

Contents

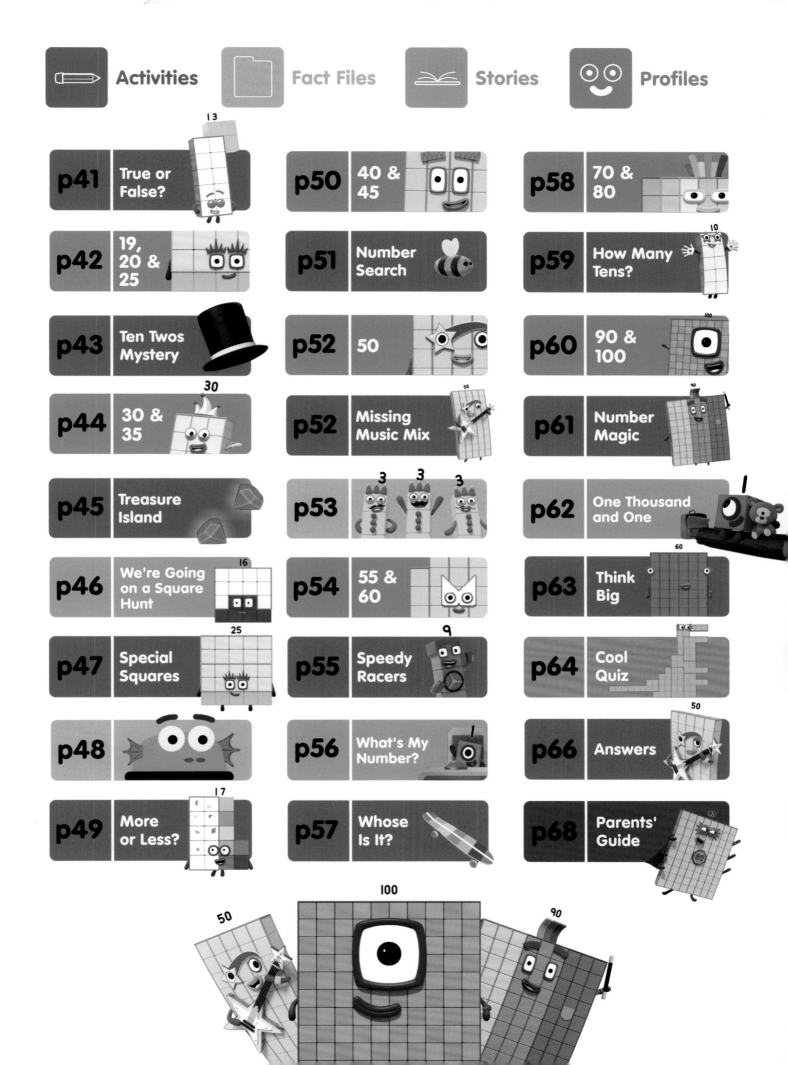

One

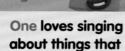

One loves singing about things that are on their own.

Her best friend is Numberblock Two.

Two

Two has two sparkly dancing shoes.

He has a special dance that goes 'One, two, one, two!'

Three

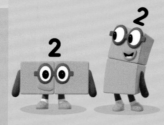

Three loves to be the star of the show!

She has three juggling balls and three triangles on her crown.

Four

Four loves squares!

His eyes and eyebrows are made of squares.

Five

Five loves giving high fives!

She has a star on her hand and a star-shaped eye.

ACTIVITY  Round Up

Four does not like round things. How many of each of these round things can you find in the scene?

Answers on p66

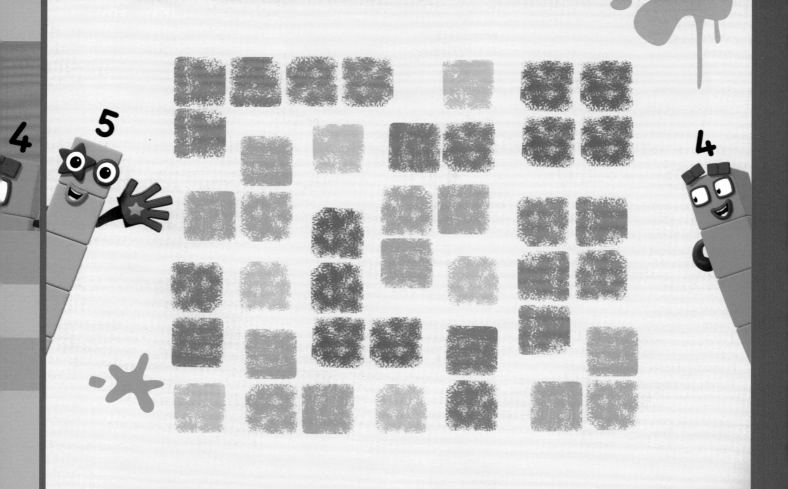

Which Numberblock made the green stamps?

Which Numberblock made the yellow stamps?

Which Numberblock made the red stamps?

Which Numberblock made the blue stamps?

The Numberblocks have stamped their shapes onto the wall. Can you count the blocks to work out who made each stamp?

Silly Stamps

ACTIVITY

Did you know? Four has a pet called Squarey!

Answers on p66

9

One

One bird.
Hello bird!

One tree.
Hello tree!

One wonderful world,
and one me!

_____ ant.
Hello ant!

One bee.
Hello bee!

One wonderful world
and one me!

When you count to one,
you can't go wrong.

Counting up to one
never takes that long.

Two

One, Two.
One, Two.
One, Two.
One, Two.

Everything is better with two.
The two of us together,
just me and you.

Imagine all the crazy things
we can do with two,
with two!

One, Two.
One, Two.
One, _____ .
One, Two.

Three

One, Two, Three,
everybody look at me.

I'm here to entertain you,
with this funky melody.

I'll juggle three balls in
the air and everyone
will cheer.

Everything's going to be
all right now number
Three is here!

Sing along with us!

Songs

10

Four

I'm Four.
Have you met me before?

I'm one more than Three,
that's plain to see.
Three plus One equals me.

I'm Four.

One, Two, _____, Four.

Can you finish these songs by guessing the missing words?

Five

Five members in my band.

One, Two, Three, Four, Five.

Five fingers on one hand.

One, Two, Three, Four, Five.

High five, high five,
high five, high five.

High five, high five,
high five, high five.

To the side. Up above.
Down low... too slow!

High _____ !

4

Who Sang That?

ACTIVITY

Sing along to the songs. Then look at the lines below. Can you guess whose song each line came from?

A — Three plus One equals me.

B — Down low... too slow!

C — When you count to one, you can't go wrong.

D — Imagine all the crazy things we can do with...

TOOT!

The Terrible Twos

Number of blocks: Two blocks each.

Special feature: They have masks that match their shoes.

Favourite thing: Being cheeky and making trouble!

Did you know: Numberblock Four splits into the Terrible Twos.

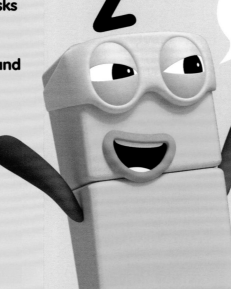

How many Twos is too many Twos, amigo?

 + =

Two   plus   Two   equals   Four

 **What Did the Twos Do?**

ACTIVITY

That was a great trick!

The Terrible Twos have played a trick on Numberblock Five. Can you work out what they have done?

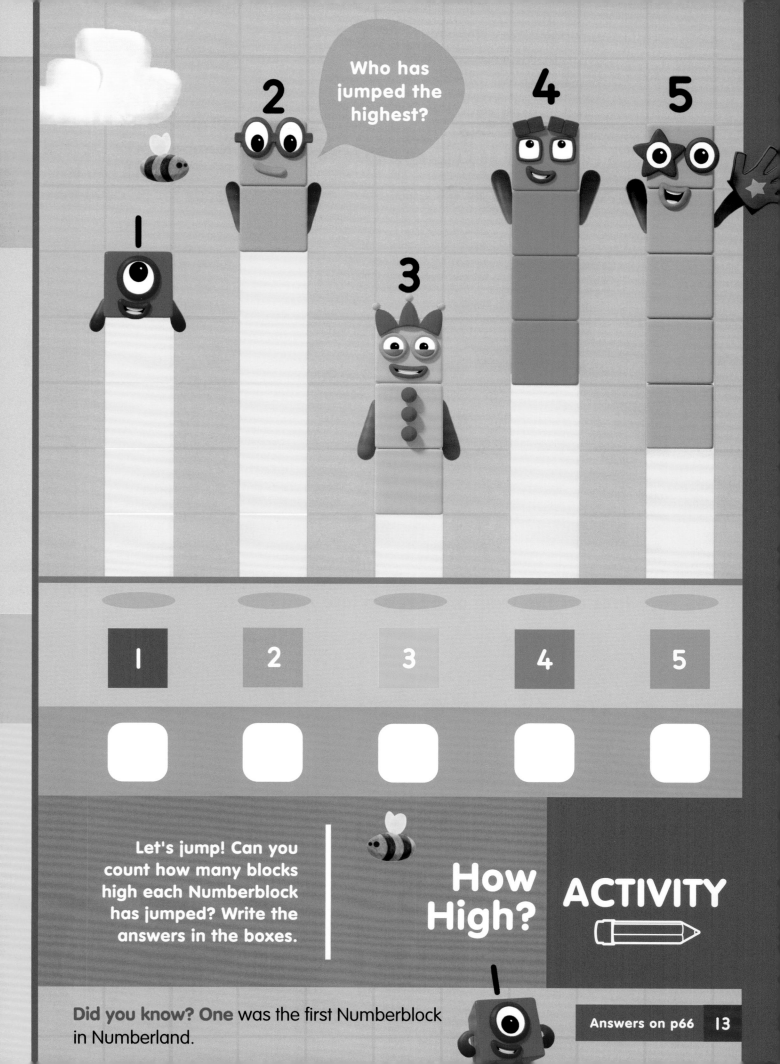

Who has jumped the highest?

Let's jump! Can you count how many blocks high each Numberblock has jumped? Write the answers in the boxes.

How High?

ACTIVITY

Did you know? One was the first Numberblock in Numberland.

STORY

The Numberblocks Express

All aboard the Numberblocks Express! Numberblock Five is ready for an adventure!

Choo-choo! Numberblock Five is driving the Numberblocks Express. She is the only one who can drive the train.

But then...

We have to stop the train. How do we make Five again?

Hop, hop, hop on top!

Five **falls off the train and breaks into five Ones.**

One plus One equals Two.

Four plus One equals...

... **Five!**

Oh no! It's the end of the line!

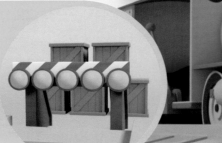

14

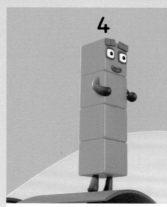

3

Two plus One equals Three.

4

Three plus One equals Four.

Five pulls on the brake. The train stops just in time. Well done, Five!

High Five!

ACTIVITY

Which of the following add up to 5?

A  + = ☐

B 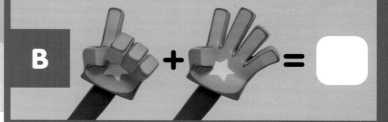 + = ☐

C 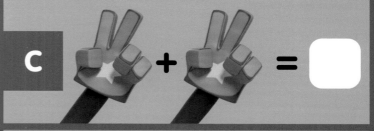 + = ☐

D  + = ☐

5

Bonus Question: Which of the Numberblocks wears glasses?

Answers on p66 15

Six

Let's roll!

Six loves to rhyme, rap and play games!

She has six dots, like the dots on a dice.

Seven

Seven can make rainbows appear!

He is very lucky and loves to help his friends.

Eight

Octoblock to the rescue!

Eight is a superhero called Octoblock!

He battles a baddy called Octonaughty.

Mirror magic...

Numberblock One sees anothe[r] One in the magic mirror! What [do] 2 Ones equal? Let's count them[.]

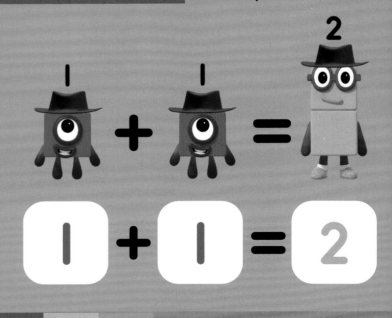

$$1 + 1 = 2$$

Now it's your turn!

Bonus Question: Which of the Numberblocks likes to juggle?

A

| 2 | + | 2 | = | |

Write your answer here.

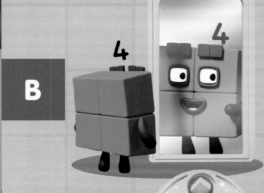

B

| 4 | + | | = | |

C

| | + | 3 | = | |

Let's step inside the
Double Dungeon of Doom!
Can you work out who these
Numberblocks will become
when they double up?

Magic Mirror

ACTIVITY

Did you know? Eight has eight tentacles.

$$5 + 4 = 9$$

Nine is a member of Square Club.

When he sneezes, he splits into **One** and **Eight**.

$$5 + 5 = 10$$

Ten can turn into a rocket and blast into space!

She has ten blocks and ten fingers.

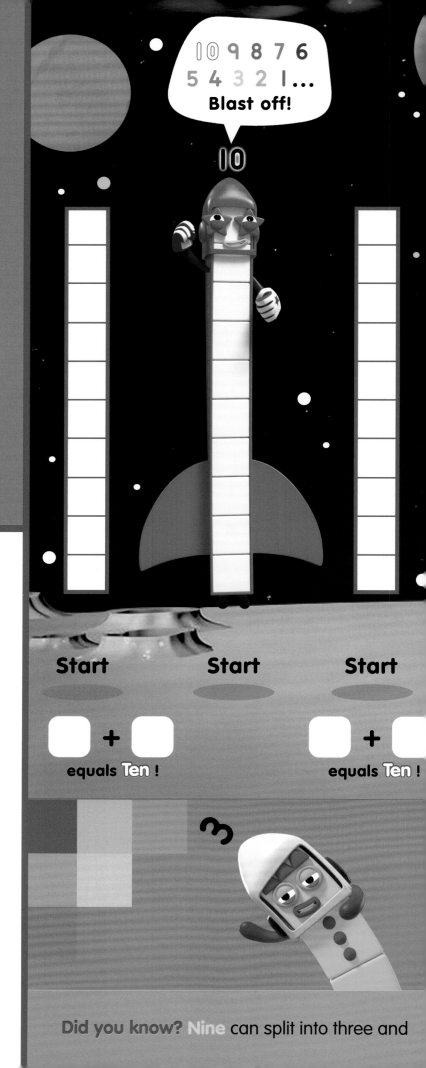

10 9 8 7 6 5 4 3 2 1...
Blast off!

Start   Start   Start

☐ + ☐   ☐ + ☐

equals **Ten** !   equals **Ten** !

Did you know? **Nine** can split into three and

Two more Tens need to enter the space race. Which of the Numberblocks above add up to 10? Colour in the blocks to help work out the answer.

SPACE RACE

ACTIVITY

become the Three Threes!

One, Two and Three share some tasty cakes.

Three **3** eats 1 cake.

Two **2** eats 1 cake.

Now there are no cakes left.

One **1** eats 1 cake.

Zero doesn't have any blocks.

Zero makes everything disappear.

There are zero instruments,

zero trees and zero gravity!

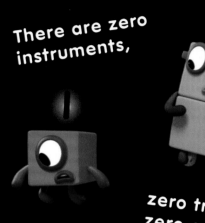
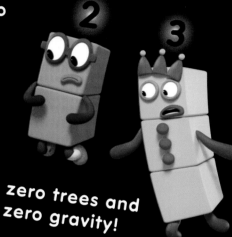

Then...
ZERO WORLDS!

One wonderful world!

Numberland reappears. Phew!

STORY Zero

Say hello to Numberblock Zero – the Numberblock with no blocks!

Quick Quiz: How many cakes did Numberblock Three eat?

What is one less than One?

Zero!

0

Oh no!

Zero has made Numberland disappear.

One has an idea.

Zero, One, Two and Three sing a song, all about nothing!

0

Which Equals Zero?

ACTIVITY

Which of the following subtractions equals 0?

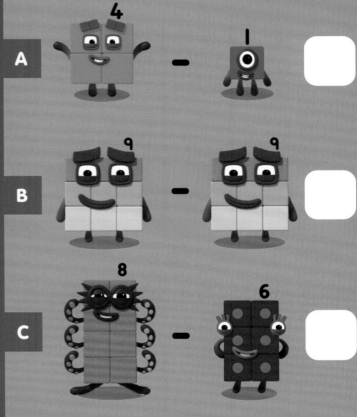

A   4 − 1

B   9 − 9

C   8 − 6

D

Answers:

Three in a Row

Numberblocks Three and Five are playing three-in-a-row. Can you see where Five needs to place her block to win each game? Draw a blue block in the right spaces.

My blocks are blue.

5

Example

A

3

B

C

It's your turn, Five!

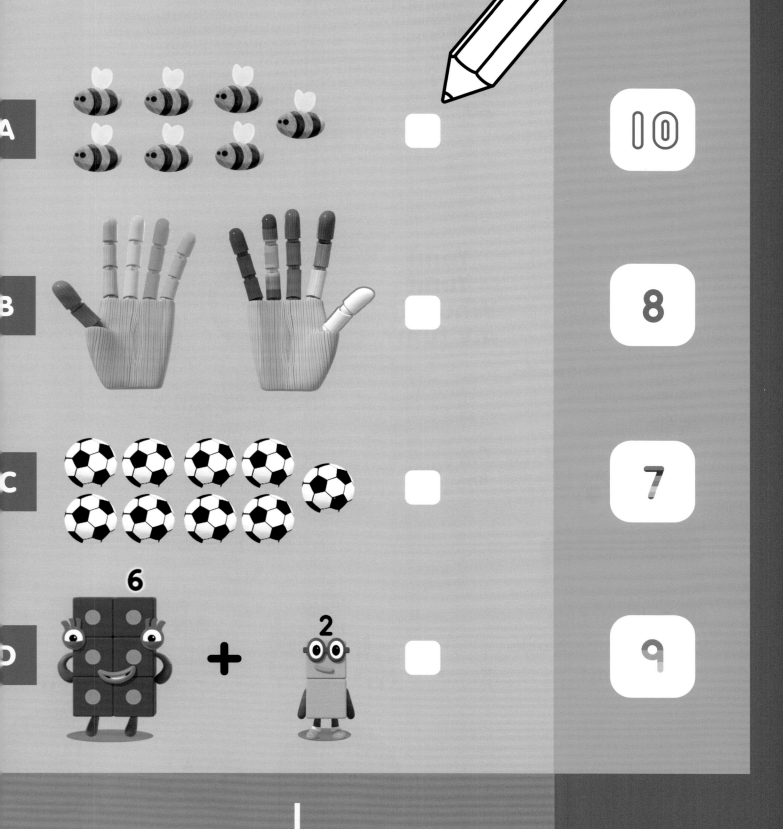

A — [ ]

B — [ ]

C — [ ]

6 + 2 — **D** — [ ]

10

8

7

9

Can you match the items on the left to the numbers on the right? Draw a line to connect them.

Matching Maths

ACTIVITY

Did you know? Seven is really lucky!

FACT FILE

Big Tum

Special feature: His big fluffy tummy.

Super skill: Gobbling up Numberblocks!

Favourite thing: Making puzzles and sequences with the Numberblocks.

> Yum! Yum! Who's in my tum?

Did you know: Big Tum lives at the top of Blocky Mountain.

Big Tum can hide lots of Numberblocks in his tummy!

ACTIVITY ✏️ Yum Yum Big Tum

Follow the clues to find out which Numberblock is hiding in Big Tum's tummy!

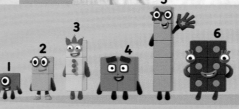

> I am smaller than Six.

> I love squares!

> I have green blocks.

A: 2   4   5

B: 9   8   6

C: 6   8   10

Yum, yum! Can you work out who's hiding in Big Tum's tummy? Write the answers on his tummy!

Big Tum Sequences

ACTIVITY

Did you know? It is cold and snowy at the top of Blocky Mountain.

Answers on p66

Eleven

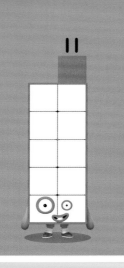

11

Eleven can make a whole football team of eleven Ones!

She loves wearing her football boots.

Twelve

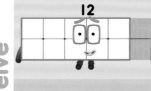

12

12

Twelve is a super rectangle!

She has rectangle rays and wears an array display watch.

Thirteen

13

Thirteen is quite clumsy and unlucky.

Every time someone says his name, his three yellow blocks fall off.

Fourteen

14

Fourteen is a super cool skater!

He can split into Lucky Double Seven.

Odd numbers

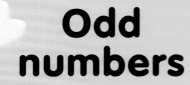

1

5

2

Even numbers

☐ ☐ ☐ ☐

13

10

Bonus Question: Which Numberblock is 5 blocks tall and 2 blocks wide?

4

6

○○○○○ ●●
○○○○○

●●
●●

○○○○○
○○○○○

●●●
●●●

The Numberblocks are going on an adventure across the seas! Put all the odd numbers into one boat and the even numbers into another.

Odds and Evens

ACTIVITY

6

Did you know? When Numberblocks stand two blocks wide, even numbers have flat tops.

Answers on p66

STORY

The Wrong Number

Oh no! **Numberblock Nine** has had his apartment broken into. Put your detective hat on and help **One** solve the case!

Time: Just before lunch
Location: Detective One's office

Another grey day in the big city!

The case of:

The Wrong Number

But then...

Detective One! I've been **ROBBED!**

Later, downtown...

Location: Nine's apartment

A mystery! **Numberblock One** gets out her notepad. 'Take me to the crime scene, **Nine**!'

Answer: Nine

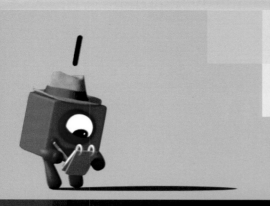

ne thinks
here's something
trange about this
umber nine.

9

What if the nine is really a...

6

6

SIX!

Silly Numberblock Nine had gone into the wrong apartment! He had not been robbed after all!

Case closed!

Guess Who

ACTIVITY

Can you help Detective One work out who these Numberblocks are?

Bonus Question:
Which of these Numberblocks is unlucky?

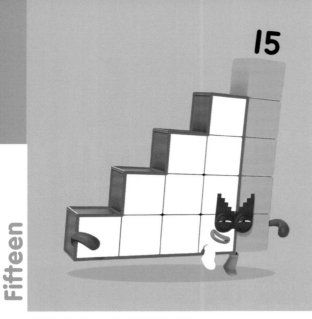

Fifteen

$$15 = 10 + 5$$

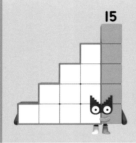

Fifteen is a super special secret agent!

She is shaped like steps and splits into the Step Squad.

Sixteen

$$16 = 10 + 6$$

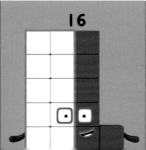

Sixteen is a party square, with lots of party tricks!

She is very good at halving and doubling.

ACTIVITY

Sharing Is Caring

Welcome to the Lair of Shares. Can you share these 16 gems equally between the 4 treasure chests?

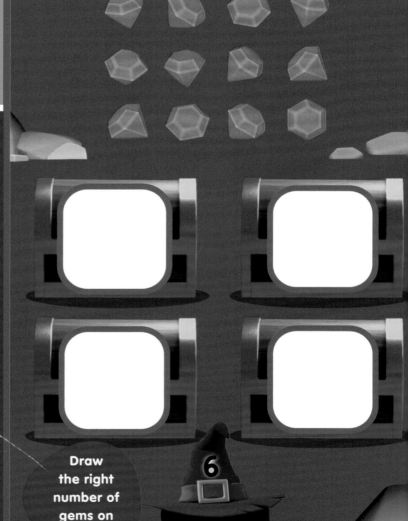

Draw the right number of gems on each chest.

Answers on p66

Square Club

Rules: No round things!

Special feature: They are all square numbers.

Favourite thing: Having square parties.

We're as tall as we are wide. We're the same turned on each side!

Read more about Square Club on page 46.

Square Club Members

1 4 9 16

ACTIVITY

Square Search

Squares have four equal sides. Count the sides of each shape to find the squares.

ACTIVITY

Can you choose the correct Numberblock to make the bridges balance?

Balancing Bridges

Example...

Fifteen balances the bridge. There are the same number of blocks on each side.

15

=

15

Now it's your turn...

A

11

12

13

12

Which Numberblock is needed to balance the bridge?

32

15

Bonus Activity: Add an equals symbol when the bridge is balanced.

10

5

2

3

1

15

Which Numberblock is needed to balance the bridge?

10

9

6

4

14

Which two Numberblocks are needed to balance the bridge?

The What-iffer takes Two on an adventure.

Imagine that!

Where am I?

One and Two are thinking big thoughts. What if Two had been the first Numberblock in Numberland?

Another Two falls from the sky to make Four!

And another Two, to make Six!

And another, to make Eight!

And another Two is Ten!

Twelve... Fourteen... Sixteen...

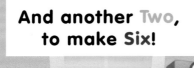

Sixteen has an idea.

Pairs party!

But Two misses his odd-number friends.

What if it rained Ones?

Imagine that!

STORY

Twoland

Get ready for a magical adventure into Twoland, with the What-iffer!

Welcome to Twoland!

Sixteen splits into Twos. They pair up to make Fours.

Then Eights. Then Sixteen again!

uddenly, Two pops back to Numberland.

He's glad to be back. Twoland was fun, but there was One important thing missing.

Imagine That ACTIVITY

The What-iffer is making Fives fall from the sky! What will the Numberblocks below become when Five lands on them?

17

Seventeen is a great artist!

He loves painting seventeen things at once, all in different colours.

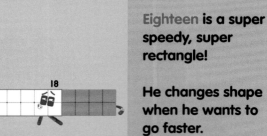

18

Eighteen is a super speedy, super rectangle!

He changes shape when he wants to go faster.

1 Let's go on a walk!

Start

2 This is going to be cool!

Start

3 This path looks a bit rocky...

Start

You bump into Three.

$1 + 3 = \boxed{}$

Two stops and says 'Hi!'

$4 + 2 = \boxed{}$

3

2

Look who's behind the tree!

$6 + 4 = \boxed{}$

Finish

Three shows you her juggling skills.

$1 + 3 = \boxed{}$

3

You meet Five at the top of Blocky Mountain.

$4 + 5 = \boxed{}$

5

Oh no! Who has Big Tum eaten from the sum?

$9 + 2 = \boxed{}$

Finish

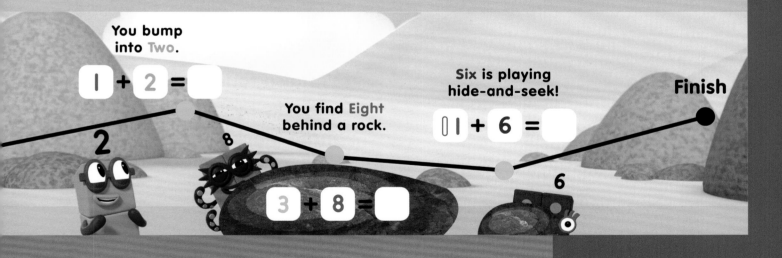

You bump into Two.

$1 + 2 = \boxed{}$

2

You find Eight behind a rock.

$3 + 8 = \boxed{}$

8

Six is playing hide-and-seek!

$1 + 6 = \boxed{}$

6

Finish

Let's go on an adventure! Choose a path for One to follow. See if you can solve the sums along the way.

Three Paths

ACTIVITY

Did you know? Eighteen loves riding the rectangle rays!

18

Answers on p66 **37**

Super Rectangles

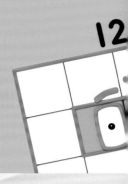

Who can be a super rectangle?

Any Numberblock who can make six different rectangles using their blocks, can be a super rectangle.

Special feature: Their rectangle rays!

Favourite thing: Their array displays.

> Look at us and be amazed. We all have rectangle rays!

> I'm a special type of rectangle. I'm a square!

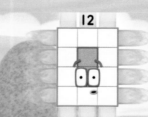

I'm three blocks by four blocks.

I'm also four blocks by three blocks.

ACTIVITY Rectangle Rays

Twelve needs to make a rectangle shape to get her rays. Circle the pose where she makes a rectangle shape.

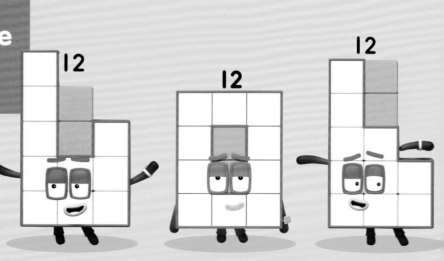

8

6

Draw in this space

Can you think of other ways **Six** and **Eight** could make rectangle shapes? Use the grid to draw them in different rectangle poses.

Rectangle Grid

ACTIVITY

Did you know? A rectangle with two long and two short sides is called an oblong.

12

Octonaughty

You've met your match, Octoblock!

Who is Octonaughty?
He's the naughtiest Numberblock in Numberland!

Number of blocks: Eight pink blocks.

Special feature: He has a green mask to match his eight green tentacles.

Favourite thing: Making trouble!

 = + + + +

 **ACTIVITY** **Who Am I?**

Octonaughty has tickled the Numberblocks and their numberlings have fallen off! Can you help put them back?

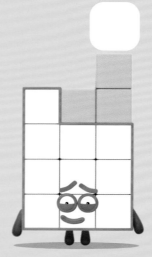

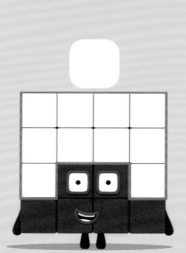

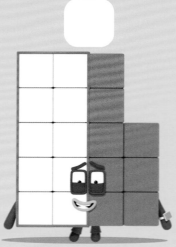

Can you work out which of these facts are true and which are false? If true, put a tick in the box. If false, put a cross.

1 One is a square, like Four and Sixteen.

2 Twelve can be made by adding two Sevens together.

3 Thirteen is very lucky.

4 Four has a pet called Squarey.

5 Fifteen can split into the Step Squad.

6 Sixteen is a member of Square Club.

7 Seventeen has nine rainbow-coloured blocks.

8 Eight is also known as Octoblock.

9 When Nine sneezes, he turns into One and Eight.

Did you know? Octonaughty once fell into a giant custard pie!

Answers on p66

19

> I can make lots of crazy shapes!

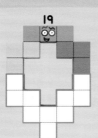

19

Nineteen changes into lots of shapes.

Her magic pencil draws funny faces on her shapes.

Twenty

10   **10**

20

Twenty loves to dance the Two Tens Tango and the Ten Twos Hot Shoe Shuffle.

Just like Two, Numberblock Twenty loves his dancing shoes!

25

> I'm as tall as I am wide!

25

Twenty-five is a square.

She can make patterns using her blocks.

CLUE ONE

$$5 + 3 = ?$$

The culprit left this clue. What could it mean?

CLUE TWO

This Numberblock is very naughty

> Help me find my hat before the show starts!

Did you know? **Twenty** is also a Super Rectangle

CLUE THREE

8

This is the silhouette of the culprit. Who could it be?

CLUE FOUR

This was found near where the hat was last seen.

CLUE FIVE

They had pink blocks and green arms.

Detective One thought she saw who took the hat.

Who has the hat? _ _ _ _ _ _ _ _ _ _

The Ten Twos Hot Shoe Shuffle group are about to perform. But one hat is missing! Oh no! Follow the clues to work out who has taken Two's hat.

Ten Twos Mystery

ACTIVITY

20

Thirty

I am Thirty. The big entertainer!

30

$$30 = 10 + 10 + 10$$

Thirty does super circus tricks.

She has a magical hat that turns into a circus tent!

35

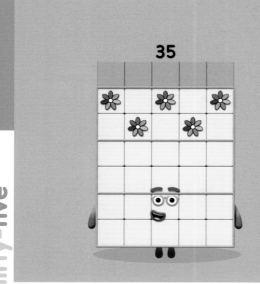

$$35 = 30 + 5$$

35

Thirty-five has rainbow-coloured flowers on his blocks.

He is made of five **Sevens** or seven **Fives**.

Bonus Question: How many Numberblocks are looking for the treasure?

5

15

The Numberblocks are searching for treasure! Draw a line from the smallest Numberblock to the largest to get to the treasure.

Treasure Island

ACTIVITY

Did you know? Twenty is an even number, and part of the Even Tops group.

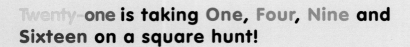

Twenty-one is taking One, Four, Nine and Sixteen on a square hunt!

Wow! An ancient temple!

Look at all those squares!

Inside...

Inside...

There are pictures of One, Four, Nine, Sixteen and... another square.

A new Numberblock appears!

Hello! I'm Twenty-five! I'm a really big square!

STORY
We're Going on a Square Hunt

Join Square Club on an adventure to an ancient temple, to find more squares!

Quick Quiz: What is 5 lots of 5?

But the tiles have fallen off. The mystery square is five lots of **Five**.

Square Club put the missing pieces back on the wall. It makes a square with twenty-five blocks!

The Square Club continue their search for more squares. With Square Club, the adventures never stop!

25

Special Squares

ACTIVITY

Fill in the gaps!

A

I am a square.
I am _____ blocks wide,
by _____ blocks tall.

16

B

I am a square.
I am _____ blocks wide,
by _____ blocks tall.

25

Blockzilla

Special feature: Her mouth, which can change shape.

Super skill: Knowing which Numberblocks are bigger or smaller than others.

Favourite thing: Playing with the Numberblocks!

Best quote: 'Me like big things!'

ROAR!

> Greater than

< Less than

= Equal

5 > 3
Five is **greater than** Three.

3 < 4
Three is **less than** Four.

4 = 4
Four is **equal** to Four.

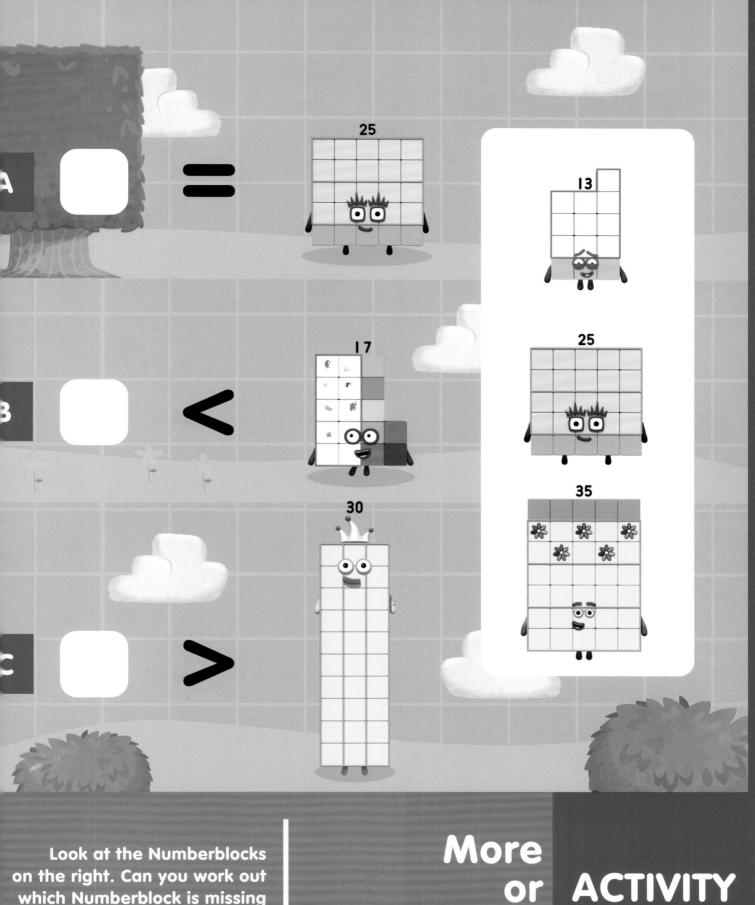

A ☐ = **25**

B ☐ < **17**

C ☐ > **30**

13

25

35

Look at the Numberblocks on the right. Can you work out which Numberblock is missing from each of the equations?

More or Less?

ACTIVITY ✏️

35

Did you know? Thirty-five is made of five Sevens.

I am **Forty**. I love rectangles!

40

$$40 = 10 + 10 + 10 + 10$$

Forty has a pet called Oblongy.

He collects different types of rectangles in his special scrapbook.

Step this way!

45

$$45 = 40 + 5$$

Forty-five has a step-shaped mask, just like **Fifteen**.

She can split into nine **Fives**.

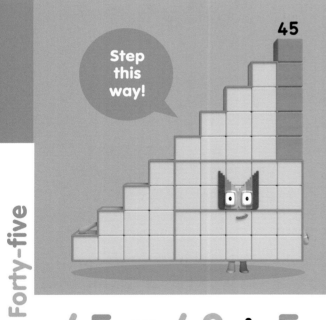

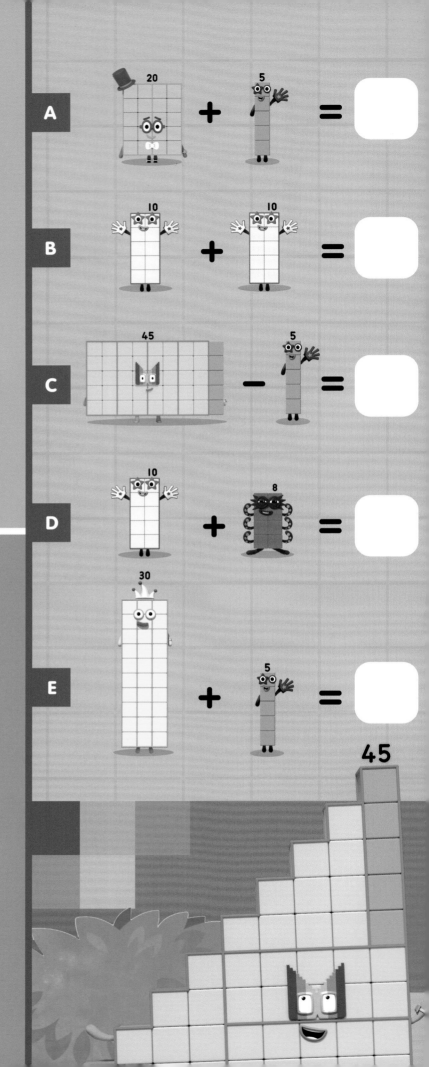

A   20 + 5 =

B   10 + 10 =

C   45 − 5 =

D   10 + 8 =

E   30 + 5 =

45

Can you work out the answers to these equations? Then try to find the answers in the scene.

Number Search

ACTIVITY

Did you know? Forty can turn into the Terrible Twenties!

Answers on p66   51

Bonus Question: Which other Numberblocks have star-shaped eyes?

I am Fifty. Let's rock!

50

Fifty

$$50 = 10 + 10 + 10 + 10 + 10$$

50

Fifty is a rock-and-roll superstar!

She plays a star-shaped gold guitar.

ACTIVITY

Missing Music Mix

Numberblock **Fifty** is putting on a show! Help her sing her favourite song by filling in the gaps.

My name is **Fifty**.
I'm a rock-and-roll superstar!

So you don't forget my name,
I play this counting game... in fives!

5, 10, ☐, 20, 25, ☐, 35, 40, ☐ and 50.

50

Answers on p66

The Three Threes

> Roll up, roll up, roll up! We are the Three Threes.

3   **3**   **3**

When do they appear? Nine splits into the Three Threes when he needs some extra help.

Special feature: They are amazing acrobats!

Favourite thing: Doing cool acrobatic tricks.

$$+ \quad + \quad = 9$$

plus   plus   equals Nine

ACTIVITY **Balloon Riddle**

$$9 \div 3 = \boxed{}$$

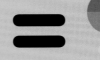

Nine has nine balloons. He wants to share them equally between the Three Threes. How many balloons should he give each Three?

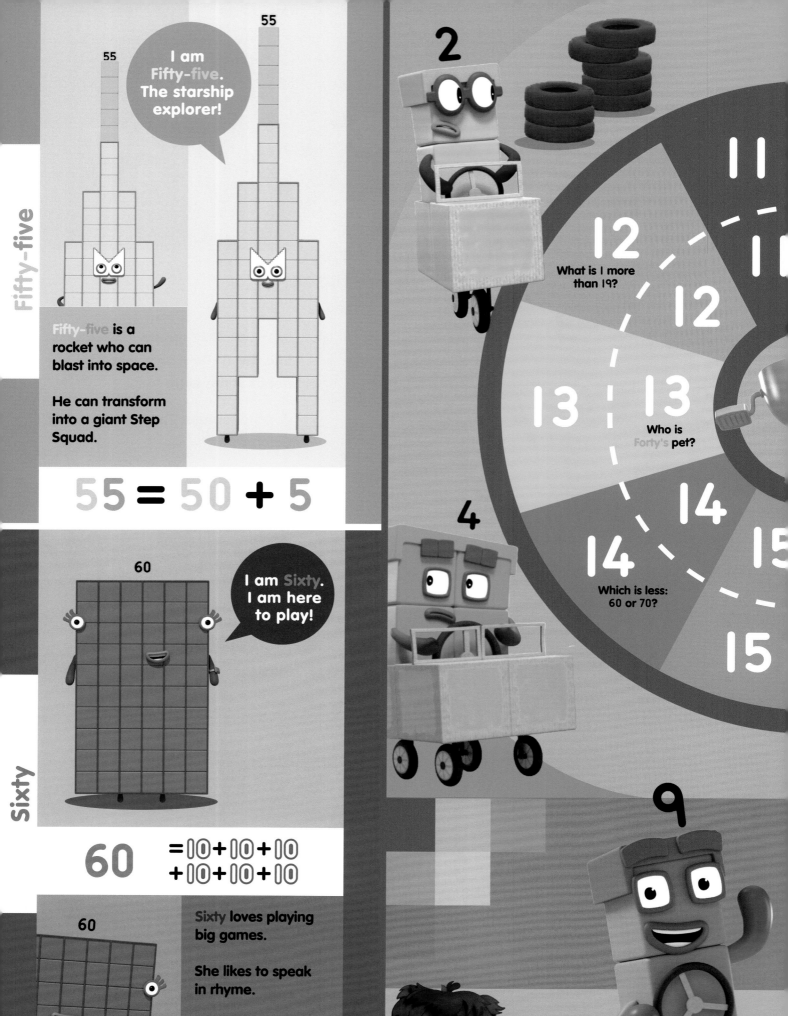

Fifty-five

I am Fifty-five. The starship explorer!

55

55

Fifty-five is a rocket who can blast into space.

He can transform into a giant Step Squad.

$$55 = 50 + 5$$

Sixty

60

I am Sixty. I am here to play!

$$60 = 10+10+10+10+10+10$$

60

Sixty loves playing big games.

She likes to speak in rhyme.

2

11

11

12

12

What is 1 more than 19?

13

13

12

Who is Forty's pet?

4

14

14

14

Which is less: 60 or 70?

15

15

9

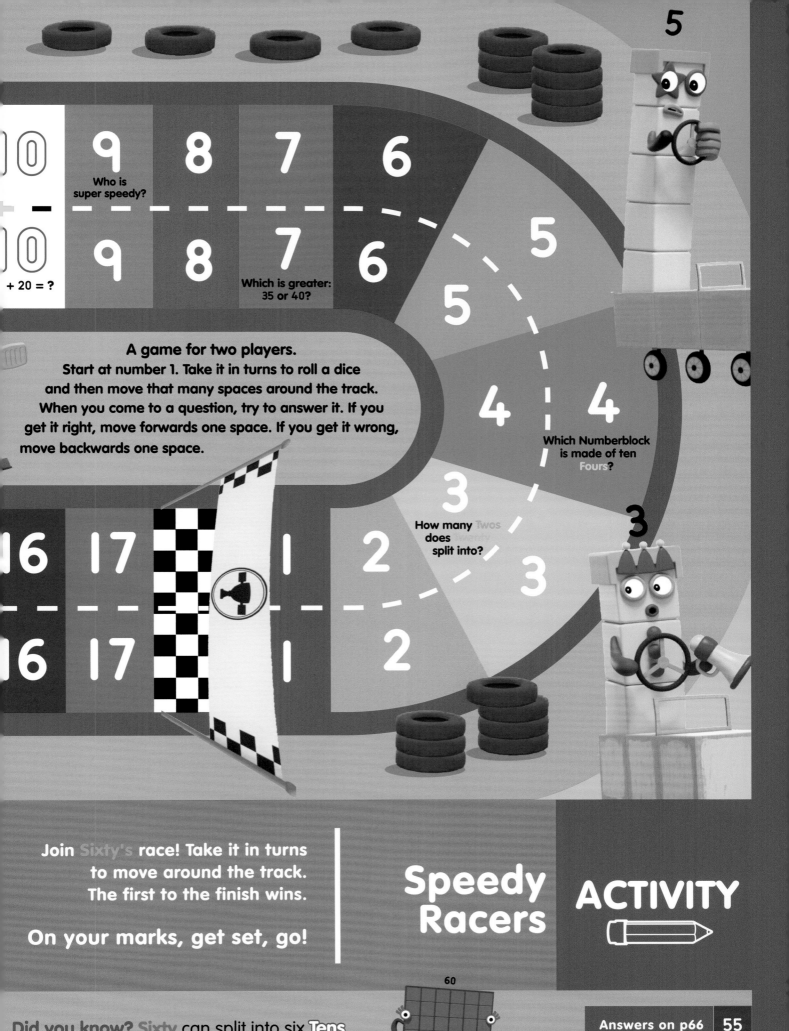

9 8 7 6

Who is super speedy?

9 8 7 6

Which is greater: 35 or 40?

10 − 10 + 20 = ?

5

5

4 4

Which Numberblock is made of ten Fours?

3

3

How many Twos does Twenty split into?

3

A game for two players.
Start at number 1. Take it in turns to roll a dice and then move that many spaces around the track. When you come to a question, try to answer it. If you get it right, move forwards one space. If you get it wrong, move backwards one space.

16 17 1 2

16 17 1 2

Join Sixty's race! Take it in turns to move around the track. The first to the finish wins.

On your marks, get set, go!

Speedy Racers

ACTIVITY

60

Did you know? Sixty can split into six Tens.

Welcome to What's My Number?

In round one, the team has to work out who's hiding. But they must not count. They must see the amount!

6

6

Who's behind the door?

That's **Five**!

Five and one... that's **Six**!

One less than ten is... **Nine**!

Six stars on the board. To win, they need ten stars.

The Numberblocks have to say how many of each object they see.

One cuddly toy.   **Two** red apples.   **Three** rubber ducks.   **Four** frogs.   **Five** paper cups.   **Six** bulls.   **Seven** bricks.

STORY

What's My Number?

Six is hosting a game show, all about numbers! One, Two and Three are on the team.

6

Quick Quiz: How many frogs were seen in round three?

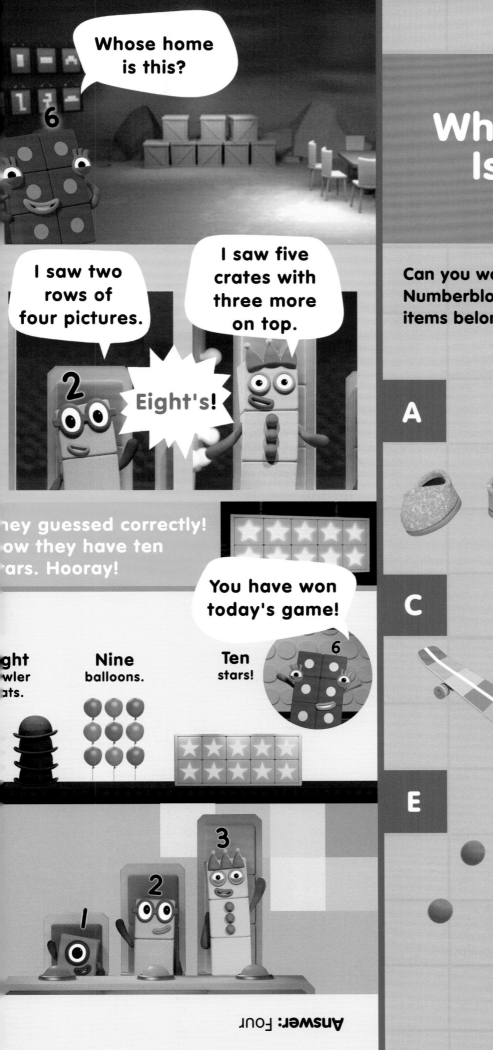

Can you work out which Numberblocks the following items belong to?

A

B

C

D

E

F

Answers on p66

I am Seventy. You lucky numbers!

70

$$70 = 10+10+10+10+10+10+10$$

70

Seventy is really lucky.

He can make rainbows from his blocks, just like Seven.

Super Octoblock to the rescue!

80

80

80

$$80 = 10+10+10+10+10+10+10+10$$

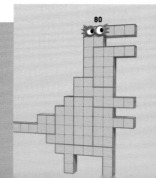

80

Eighty has a pink cape and badge.

He can transform into Dinoctoblock, Roboctoblock and Spidoctoblock!

I am Thirty!

30

EXAMPLE...

How many Tens is Numberbloc Thirty made out of? Let's coun

$$10 + 10 + 10 = 30$$

Thirty is made of three Tens.

10

Did you know? Numberblock Eighty is a

Now it's your go!

40

A _____ Tens.

50

B _____ Tens.

80

C _____ Tens.

60

D _____ Tens.

Can you work out how many Tens each of these big Numberblocks are made of?

How Many Tens?

ACTIVITY

80

superhero, like Eight!

90

I am Ninety. You won't believe your eyes!

$90 = 10+10+10+10+10+10+10+10+10$

90

90

Ninety can do amazing magic tricks.

He always carries his magic wand with him.

Number magic...

There are six flowers. Ninety waves his magic wand and then there are four flowers. How many flowers did Ninety make disappear?

$$6 - 2 = 4$$

Six flowers minus two flowers equals four flowers.

One Hundred

Think BIG!

100

$100 = 10+10+10+10+10+10+10+10+10+10$

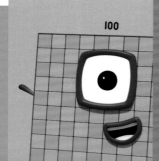

100

One Hundred is made of one hundred Ones.

She likes to teach the Numberblocks all about big numbers.

Did you know? Ninety is ten blocks less than

Now it's your go!

A

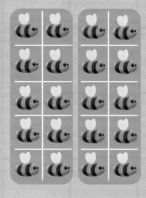 

How many bees disappeared?

B

How many footballs disappeared?

C

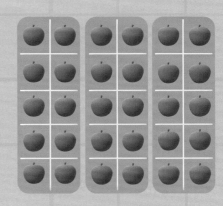 

How many apples disappeared?

Ninety is making objects disappear in tens! Can you work out how many of each item Ninety has made disappear?

Number Magic

ACTIVITY

90

One Hundred.

One, **Ten** and One Hundred are camping in the woods. One thinks that there are one hundred stars in the sky. One Hundred says there are many more.

One thinks about the biggest number she knows: One Hundred!

What's one bigger than Nine Hundred and Ninety-nine?

I'm One Thousand. I'm a thousand Ones!

1000

Ten Thousand

One Hundred Thousand

and ONE MILLION!

One is so tired from her big thoughts that she falls asleep. She dreams about REALLY BIG numbers. Like...

STORY

One Thousand and One

One, Ten and One Hundred are going camping. What new numbers will they discover on their trip?

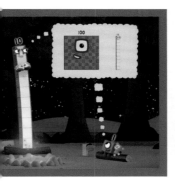

en thinks about adding tens to make EVEN BIGGER numbers.

One Hundred thinks about adding hundreds to make REALLY BIG numbers.

One realises that she can always think of a bigger number. Numbers go on forever!

Think Big ACTIVITY

Place the Numberblocks below in the correct order, going from the smallest to the largest.

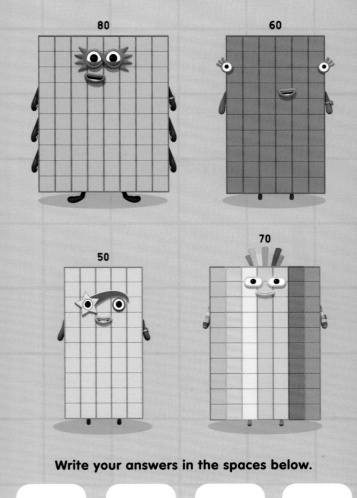

80

60

50

70

Write your answers in the spaces below.

Smallest ———→ Largest

QUIZ

It's time for the Numberblocks quiz! How well do you know your numbers? Put a tick in the correct box.

Cool Quiz

Question 1

Which of these Numberblocks are in Square Club?

| A | Four, Nine, Sixteen | | B | Two, Six, Ten | |
| C | Three, Seven, Thirteen | | D | Thirty, Forty, Forty-five | |

Question 2

Who can do magic tricks using their wand?

| A | Fourteen | | B | Thirty | |
| C | Fifty | | D | Ninety | |

Question 3

How manys Tens does Seventy split into?

| A | Four | | B | Five | |
| C | Seven | | D | Nine | |

Question 4

Squarey is hiding throughout this book. How many times can you find her?

Quiz time!

60

Question 5

Who can transform into Dinoctoblock?

A Twenty		B Eighty	
C Ninety		D One Hundred	

Question 6

Who did the What-iffer take on a journey to Twoland?

A Two		B Three	
C Seven		D Thirty-five	

Question 7

Who thought their apartment had been robbed in The Wrong Number story?

A Nine		B Twenty-five	
C Fifteen		D Eight	

ANSWERS

Page 8
Red ball = **3** Sun = **1** Football = **2**

Page 9
Two made the green stamps.
Four made the red stamps.
One made the yellow stamps.
Three made the blue stamps.

Page 10
Song One - **One**
Song Two - **Two**
Song Four - **Three**
Song Five - **Five**

Page 11
A. **Four** B. **Five** C. **One** D. **Two**

Page 12
They have taken away one block!

Page 13
1 - **4** 2 - **5** 3 - **1** 4 - **3** 5 - **2**
Two jumped the highest.

Page 15
A - **4** B - **5** C - **4** D - **5**
B and D add up to **5**.
Bonus question: Two

Page 16-17
A. **2 + 2 = 4**
B. **4 + 4 = 8**
C. **3 + 3 = 6**
Bonus question: Three

Page 18-19
7 and **3**
8 and **2**
Did you work out that
5 + 3 + 2 equals Ten too?
So does **7 + 2 + 1**.

Page 21
A - **3** B - **0** C - **2** D - **0**
B and D make **0**.

Page 22

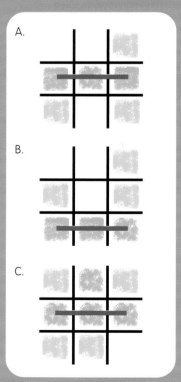

Page 23
A - **7** B - **10** C - **9** D - **8**

Page 24
Four is hiding in Big Tum's tummy!

Page 25
A - **3** B - **7** C - **4**

Page 26-27
Odd - **1, 5, 13.**
Even - **2, 4, 6, 10.**
Bonus question: Ten

Page 29
From left to right: **6, 14, 13.**
Bonus question: Thirteen

Page 30
To share the gems equally, draw four
gems on each chest.

Page 31
There are **two** squares.

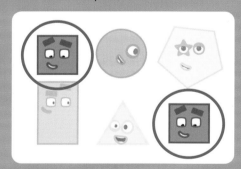

Page 32-33
A - **12**   B - **5**   C - **10** and **4**

Page 35
11 will become **16**.
9 will become **14**.

Page 36-37
1. **1 + 3 = 4,   4 + 2 = 6,   6 + 4 = 10.**

2. **1 + 3 = 4,   4 + 5 = 9,   9 + 2 = 11.**

3. **1 + 2 = 3,   3 + 8 = 11,   11 + 6 = 17.**

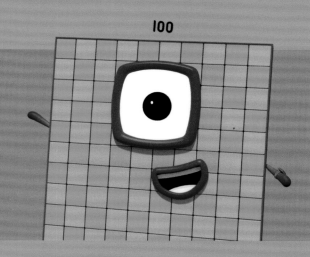

100

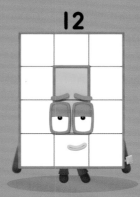

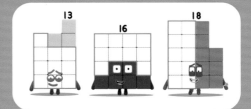
50

Parents' Guide

80

Ask Questions

While reading this annual with your child, ask lots of questions: What can they see? Can they spot any patterns? What would happen if certain Numberblocks **joined together** or **broke apart**?

Numberblock Prints

Cut out blocks from old sponges so your child can make their own **Numberblock stamps**. How many shapes can your child make with five blocks?

'One Says' Game

Shout out 'One says...' and then follow it with an activity. 'One says do one jump!', 'Three says give three hugs!' etc.

Make and Play

Make your own Numberblocks with your child or use any sort of blocks you have. Stack them up and guess how tall the stack is.

How Many?

When you're out and about, keep an eye out for **numbers**. While shopping: 'Can you find **twelve** apples?' While walking: 'Can you find **twenty** flowers?'

Mistakes

Write numbers and include deliberate mistakes for your child to spot, e.g. **switching two numbers** around in a sequence (11, 12, 13, 15, 14, 16), or writing a number back to front.

Toy Time

Arrange toys in columns and rows – 2 rows of 5, 3 rows of 4, and so on – and guess how many there are without counting. Then count them to check.

Dice and Dots

Roll two dice. Ask your child how many dots are on each, then how many there are in total, by counting or by adding. Then try three dice.

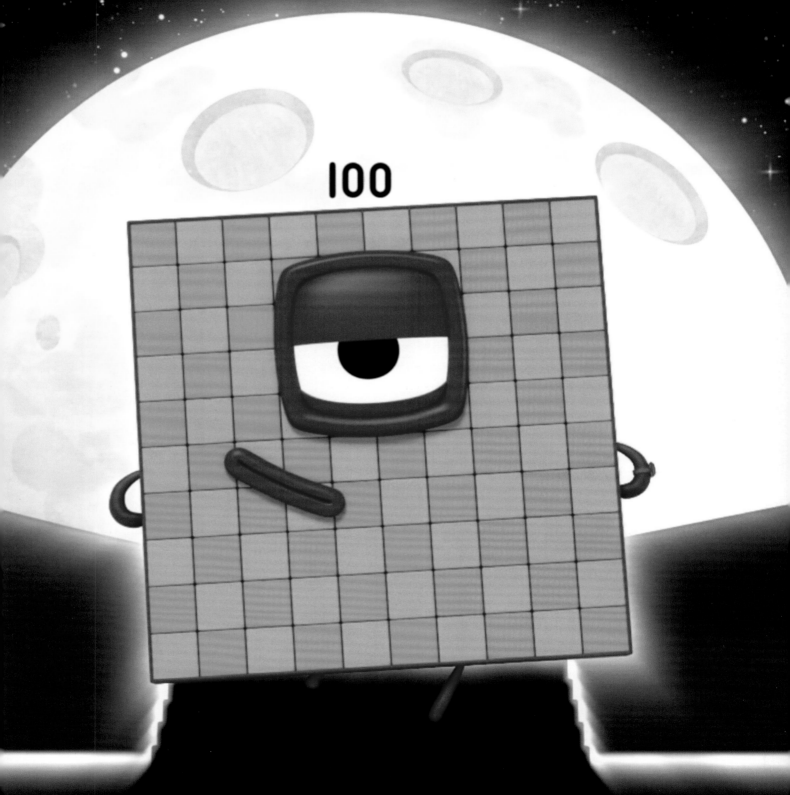

100

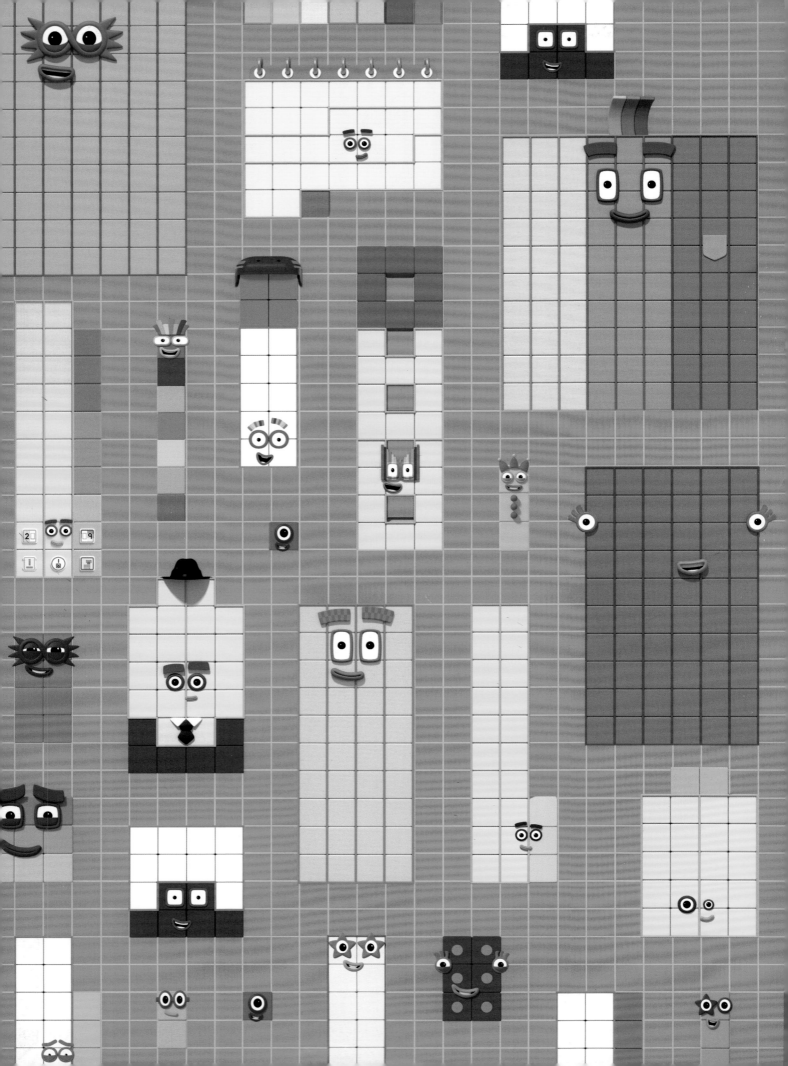